Wild White Wings

WILD WHITE WINGS

by

EMILY WATSON HALLIN

and

ROBERT KINGERY BUELL

Illustrated by LARRY TOSCHIK

DAVID McKAY COMPANY

NEW YORK

1965

Dedicated to Chief Librarian
Doris Holden
of the Palo Alto Children's Library
who so generously aided the authors
with her love and knowledge of
children and their books.

1: *Above the Arctic Circle*

THE OLD COB, FEEDING AMONG REEDS, RAISED HIS HEAD FROM the water, stretched his long neck and looked down the length of the pond. Along the shore in the distance, three dark objects moved. The Old Cob froze, sensing danger from an ancient enemy—man. Eskimo boys were hunting for birds' eggs, as their fathers and grandfathers had hunted before them. Beyond the boys the midnight sun rolled around the rim of the horizon. The sky above the polar icecap glared like silver.

The big male whistling swan sounded an alarm—an urgent call that traveled far across the Mackenzie River delta. Myriads of nesting birds became silent.

From a nest at the edge of the pond, the Old Pen heard her mate's warning. Obeying at once, she drew her black, webbed feet up onto either side of the stacked twig nest, spread her great wings and lifted her soft, warm plumage from the clutch of six eggs. Reaching out, she gathered quick beakfuls of moss and covered the eggs. Only then did the Old Pen waddle down the stick bridge to the water. Quickly she paddled past sedges and reeds to join the Old Cob.

Together, followed by an escort of eider ducks, they swam rapidly to a more remote part of the pond. It was not so far away that they lost sight of their nest. The swans' marvelous eyes, placed on either side of their heads, gave them an immense span of vision over the landscape of spongy, olive-green vegetation.

The Eskimo boys who approached in the distance came from a camp farther down the river. Their fathers were away for the day, whaling. Long sticks the boys carried were used to poke into mossy mounds. Although the Arctic night was warm, the boys wore the hoods of their parkas up about their heads as protection from clouds of mosquitoes that hovered over the ponds.

The whistling swans saw the boys come close to the nest, and their alarm increased. The Old Pen shivered. One of the boys had prodded the nest with his stick.

A shout came drifting across the water: "Krugluk!" That was the Eskimo word for whistling swan. The oldest boy, Quupak, had made the find. His friends hurried to his side.

Ningarsik, the smallest boy, snatched off the moss that covered the six creamy eggs. Quupak grabbed Ningarsik's hand. A sudden thought had come to him.

"Wait," he ordered. "We must leave the eggs to hatch."

The other boys made sour faces. "We're hungry," said one defiantly.

"The Brush Man of the Loucheaux will get you if you touch the eggs of the Krugluk," Quupak chided, wagging his fingers in the face of Ningarsik.

The small boy's face screwed up in fear at the mention of the yellow-eyed monster of Arctic legend.

"The Brush Man of the Loucheaux does not care about the Krugluk," the middle boy, Paasaak, interrupted.

"But, Paasaak," Quupak's face became serious, "in school at Inuvik we learn about birds. Whistling swans are special. Hunters may not shoot them. I want these eggs to hatch. We will go hunt eggs of ducks and geese and other birds.

"And," he continued, "maybe if the eggs hatch I can get a baby whistling swan. I could take him to Inuvik with me when I go back to school."

Ningarsik and Paasaak had no time to renew their arguments in favor of taking the eggs. A throbbing sound distracted them.

The Old Cob and the Pen, at the other side of the pond, heard it, too. They turned their attention from the boys to focus on this new disturbance at the top of the world. The steady throb grew gradually louder.

The three Eskimo boys looked out toward the river channel.

"The motorboat!" Paasaak exclaimed.

"Father!" shouted Quupak. Quupak was proud that his father owned a motorboat. Some Eskimo men still hunted in kayaks.

The boys now turned from the nest and half waded and half walked through the swampy land that lay between the pond and the river.

Out in the channel toward Richards Island, a few chunks of ice still churned in the waves. The cold surf rolled in and splashed its foam on the rocks. The sound of the approaching motor became more distinct. The boys saw that the boat was pulling a dark object.

"They are towing a whale!" Paasaak exclaimed. The boys' eagerness mounted as the gap between boat and shore narrowed. They ran along the shore shouting.

A shot rang out across the water. It was a greeting from Quupak's father to the Eskimos waiting in the camp.

Back on the pond, the Old Cob and the Old Pen heard the shot from the Eskimo's gun. They trembled. It was a sound they seldom heard here in the Arctic; in other places, as they made their way southward for the winter, they had heard it. They feared it above all other sounds. The swans huddled together, motionless, with the eider ducks forming a semicircle around them. The little flotilla, with the tall sedge grasses behind it, was reflected in the icy stillness of the pond.

The boys still splashed along the marshy shore, rocking from side to side as their boots oozed into the muskeg. For the time, the swans' nest was forgotten. They thought only of reaching the campsite to welcome the boat and the whale. The swans watched them until they disappeared from sight.

2: Fighting Wings

THE OLD PEN HEADED FOR THE SEDGES ACROSS THE POND, paddling with one big black foot, the other foot held straight along her side. Close behind sailed the Old Cob.

They did not swim directly to the nest, but zigzagged among the tall, reedy plants, for they must be alert for other enemies—sharp-eyed otters, foxes, eagles, ravens and jaegars. Presently the Old Pen reached the bridge of sticks. With a single stroke of her wing, she raised herself from the water and climbed up to peer at the eggs. In her anxiety one webbed foot kicked loose several sticks.

The moss cover was gone, but the eggs were safe! The Old Pen gave a soft cluck to reassure the Cob. She stretched her long neck upward, half raised her broad wings and shook herself. A shower of droplets sprang from her feathers. She preened her body carefully with her black beak, squeezing out the rest of the water so that the eggs would not get wet.

Despite her caution, as she lowered herself to brood again over the eggs, the weakened edge of the nest gave way. The Pen felt an egg roll from the nest. She raised herself again with an excited hiss that brought the Cob quickly to the shore. The Old Pen extended her neck and tried to reach

5

the egg with her beak. Again and again she stretched. The Cob waded up on shore and pushed the egg with his beak, but the egg had rolled too far. The slope of the nest was too steep. The Old Cob lost interest. The Pen, too, abandoned her attempt to rescue the egg. She rearranged the twigs and repaired the hole. Then she settled down to brood on the remaining five eggs.

The eggs had been laid late in May. July was just beginning. The cygnets should hatch any day.

For four more days the Old Pen sat on the nest. Around the foot-and-a-half-high mound of twigs and moss, the Pen had eaten off all the vegetation she could reach by extending her long neck to its limit. A few of her small feathers had dropped off and lay among the mosses and tiny flowers at the edge of the nest.

When hunger drove the Old Pen from her brooding, she called softly to her mate, who was seldom far away. There were no other swans on this pond. If any came, the Old Cob would soon drive them off. He had staked his claim here years ago, and there was just enough vegetation in such a small pond to feed his own brood of cygnets each year. He could tolerate a few ducks and geese, but not other swans.

The Old Cob had first claimed this pond when he was in his fifth spring. Flying beside him, as she had been ever since, was his newly won pen. They were about to start their first nest and raise their first cygnets. They were looking for a site.

As the young pair flew over the pond just freed from its lock of ice, they saw a lone cob on the shore. They saw him pulling out sedge stalks and heaping them helter-skelter into a pile. The lone cob had lost his mate, but still he had returned to his nesting place and was trying to build a nest. He did not succeed, because he had no pen to shape his materials into a nest.

The young swans saw a good breeding place and only a lone cob. Although the lone cob, as soon as he saw the intruding pair, flung them an angry warning note and showed them the size and power of his big, snowy wings, the young cob was not afraid. He persisted in circling the pond with his beautiful white pen beside him. The lone cob, after many angry honks and displays of his wings, rose fiercely onto his big black feet. He sailed into the air after the young swan. The young cob was strong, but not experienced. He turned and fled. The angry lone cob propelled his wings to top speed. He closed in on the young cob, who began to climb. This was his signal of surrender.

The lone cob turned back to the lake, calling triumphantly, although no mate was there to hear him. The young pen's notes as she flew were distressed. The young cob would not stay defeated in his new mate's presence. He flew in on the lone cob again.

He landed and lowered his head in signal that he was ready to fight. The lone cob advanced on him, crying out with a series of clear, clarinet-like notes, and a tremendous struggle took place. The water swirled in the air about the fighting cobs as they whacked each other with their wings and jabbed and pounded with their beaks. Sometimes one swan would get his feet up on the water and try

to trample his opponent under the surface. Each tried to
get a grip on the other's neck to pull him under the water
and drown him. White feathers flew amid cascades of water.
The young pen floated fearfully near the shore.

At last the battle ended. The young swan's need of the
pond had given him the persistence to beat the tough old
lone swan. The former owner of the pond retreated across
the water with the young cob chasing after him and taking
a few last punishing tweaks at his tail feathers. The lone
cob retired to the opposite side of the lake.

Then, tired though he was, the young cob turned in the
greatest expression of triumph a swan can display, his wings
outspread and quivering, voicing many excited notes to tell
his young mate of his victory. She advanced toward him
echoing his call of victory, nodding her head in approval
and stretching trembling wings to greet the victor. When
they met on the water, their wings and necks relaxed and
reclined. They surveyed the kingdom that was theirs and
rejoiced with wild, wailing voices. This had been their
exclusive nesting territory ever since. The young cob had
let the lone cob live at the other side of the pond until
the first cygnets had hatched, and then had chased him
away.

Through the years, intruding swan pairs had occasionally
challenged for the pond, but the young cob had battled
them off. And now, after many years, the young cob and
pen were an old cob and pen. They were raising their
twenty-fifth brood of cygnets.

As the Old Cob heard the Pen's call, he made for the

nest. After a month of waiting for the cygnets, he was impatient with his duty as guard. While he stood sentry over the nest, his eyes darted restlessly about, always keeping his mate in focus as she dived again and again in search of roots, tiny shellfish, grasses and the succulent water plants that grew in the pond bottom.

The Cob had for days stayed close to the nest, seldom trying his wings, since the hatching of the cygnets was near. Suddenly he felt a wild longing for the sky. Swimming alongside his mate, he inclined his neck toward the nest as though directing her back to it.

The Pen dived once more, gobbled a beakful of pondweed, and obediently returned to the nest.

Pushing backward with his huge black feet against the surface of the pond, the Cob ran for fifteen or twenty feet along the top of the water, which splashed and eddied in his wake. His wings flapped noisily as he beat the water. It took a good deal of momentum to get his twenty-pound body into the air. Once airborne, his feet still moved in a running motion, then were drawn up against his body as he extended his long neck straight out, his black beak pointing westward. His great white wings rose and fell in quick, short strokes as he flew joyously out beyond the pond toward the channel. Below him, as he rose, the vivid colors of the flowering tundra faded. The tundra, from the sky, took on a dun-colored hue. He saw the water churning in the channel, and beyond, Richards Island.

A few cobs from other ponds joined the Old Cob, for they had heard the delicate, musical barking sound he made as he flew. They joined their singing to his, and the combination of their voices, heard from below, sounded like a series of whistles, which the swans uttered in groups of three—oo-oo-oo. The birds formed an irregular line, with the Old Cob leading them through the bright, clear sky, their great wings dipping and rising in unison.

As the swans passed over a point of land that jutted out on the channel, the Old Cob could see the Eskimo camp below. Two boats were pulled up on the shore. A few hide tents were anchored with circles of rocks. He could see the Eskimos working on the great carcass of the whale. There were many dogs and children running about.

The men did not alarm him now, for he was in his element—the endless sky. And he was not aware of the plan in the Eskimo boy's mind of capturing one of the Old Cob's cygnets to take to his school.

The Old Cob and his flying mates, because they all had brooding pens to look after, suddenly wheeled and started back in easterly direction across the Mackenzie delta, the cobs dispersing as they arrived at their individual nesting places.

As the Old Cob descended over his pond, the scene below him revealed that he had stayed away too long. The Old Pen was not brooding on her mound of moss. Wings outspread, she stood defiantly guarding the nest. She was holding at bay a snarling brown animal.

It was a young wolverine—the most cunning and fierce of Arctic mammals. The animal struck at the Old Pen with his short front paw's barbed claws. Missing, he advanced farther up the untidy heap of stalks that was the nest.

The Old Cob was frantic. He made a low, swooping dive over the animal. Again he swerved low in a tight circle over the young wolverine, battling him with his powerful wing.

The wolverine, jaws agape, whirled from the Pen to slash at the Old Cob as he dove. Again he missed. This increased the fury of his attack on the Old Pen as the Old Cob ascended and circled for another attack. The Old Pen still held her great seven-foot wings high. They were her only means of defense. She wanted to get them away from the ugly beast—to be with her Cob in the sky.

Again the wolverine struck. His claws ripped the Old Pen's wing. As she wrested it away, a stream of blood dyed her glistening wing feathers and fell to stain the bright moss beneath her. Now the Old Pen fought for her life. She jabbed and whacked desperately. Although not designed for fighting, her wings had the power to break an animal's bones.

With angry cries, the Old Cob dove again on the lunging animal. His wings added their tremendous strength to the Old Pen's. The wolverine leaped toward the attacker. Then he turned and disappeared into the sedges.

The Cob landed on the water and streaked to his nest. What had happened? The Old Pen had not returned to her eggs. She lay beside the nest, exhausted. The Old Cob walked slowly around her. Several of the flight feathers from her wing lay scattered on the moss. The torn wing, stained with blood, lay spread along the ground. Her graceful neck drooped against the side of the nest.

As the Old Cob surveyed the damage to his mate, a crackling noise drew his head around toward the nest. A pair of dark brown eyes in a tiny grayish head peeked out at the Old Cob from a hole poked in one of the eggshells.

3: The Newcomers

THE OLD COB'S EYES DARTED FROM THE STRICKEN PEN TO THE peeping cygnet. Could he help his mate? Her head raised weakly, and then fell back to the mossy slope of the nest.

The cygnet's peep became urgent. The Cob must take the Pen's place and tend this noisy ball of feathers. As he climbed upon the nest he came near to squashing the new-hatched cygnet with a large, clumsy foot. Soon other cries would be heard from other eggs. It was a busy time for both Pen and Cob. He must do it alone and still stand guard over his wounded mate. He watched the motionless Pen anxiously. Now and then the cygnet peered curiously from beneath his father's soft feathers and peeped loudly. The father turned his mournful eyes from the Old Pen to guide his cygnet back under his feathers. It was not time for the cygnet to come out into the air. He was not dry.

The Old Pen stirred at each peep from the new cygnet. But each time she raised her head, she fell back exhausted. Old Cob felt another egg stirring beneath him. The first cygnet's peep grew increasingly shrill. The Cob recognized this as a hunger cry. But he dared not leave to dredge up a water plant for the cygnet to eat. He could feel the cygnet trying its tiny legs beneath him. If the Old Cob left the nest, the cygnet would surely wander out too soon.

13

The Old Cob heard the peeping beneath him grow louder. Now, beneath his other wing, he could feel a second cygnet struggling about. He glanced at the Old Pen.

Her large white body heaved upward in a tremendous effort as she heard the added cheep. The Cob took hope. But, weak from the loss of blood, she fell back again. Nothing stirred except her black eyes, which looked beseechingly toward the nest.

Hours passed. Still the Old Cob kept his vigil over the lively cygnets and his wounded mate. The cygnets, which now and again would appear noisily under their father's wings, were like balls of sooty brownish fluff. Their tiny, flesh-colored beaks opened and closed in a chain of hungry peeps. Old Cob saw the egg tooth of each cygnet, the tools which had enabled them to crack through the eggshell. Soon they would lose these teeth. A third cygnet, the Old Cob could feel, had joined the others. And close after the third, a fourth cygnet broke its way out of the shell.

As the two new cygnets dried themselves under the Old Cob's warmth, the Old Pen, who for many hours had not moved, stirred again.

Her long rest had restored some of her strength. Her head came up several inches from the ground. She was able to turn her body. One wing, however—the one slashed by the young wolverine—trailed uselessly beside her.

The Old Cob bent his head downward toward her as she moved. Despite the clamor of the four cygnets, the Cob padded off the nest and toward the Pen. His neck inclined downward in a gesture of devotion, as hers came up and twined about his. He waddled to the edge of the pond and into the water to pinch out a beakful of tender plants. He returned to leave them beside the Pen, and then he clambered again onto the big, conical nest.

With a painful effort, the Old Pen raised herself to peck at the food left by the Cob. Then, exerting the new strength, she stood on her feet. She wavered weakly and fell back again on the moss.

The Old Cob settled again upon the cygnets. The last two were becoming dry and fluffy. The first two clamored more noisily. One egg was not hatched. It had been cracked by the Eskimo boy's stick.

At last the Old Cob, who preferred guarding the nest to brooding on it, became impatient and again strode off the nest. The cygnets flopped about in their shallow depression of moss. The first cygnet had become steady on his tiny, yellowish legs. Seeing the great white source of his warmth disappear over the side of the nest, he wobbled up the incline after the Old Cob. The brown eyes of the second cygnet, who had more white and less of the sooty color on her than the others, followed the first cygnet as he reached the edge of the nest and tumbled down the incline of twigs and moss that made a bridge to the water. She, too, tried her day-old legs, breaking into a loud peep as she gained the top of the incline and looked out over this world of incredible color. A tiny garden of pink saxifrage grew not far from the nest, alongside a clump of crowberry bushes. The tiny cygnet looked far out through the unending daylight across the boundless sky in which she was to spend so many of her hours. No trees rose to break her view, for the cygnet's home was above treeline. As she breathed in the clear air with its scent of tundra flowers and felt the spring of the yellow moss beneath her feet, the infant swan showed her first joy at being alive in the Arctic world. She rushed pell-mell down the bridge toward the icy pond, to plunge herself into an even greater delight.

Excitement entered the Old Pen's weary body as she heard the cygnet's noisy peep and saw her scramble into the water, where the Old Cob was waiting with the first cygnet.

With that excitement coursing through her, the Old Pen forgot her wound and stood again. Her unsteady legs made it to the nest, in which she saw two balls of grayish-white down rolling about. Gently the Old Pen nudged one cygnet with her black beak, guiding it up the side of the nest toward the bridge, where its brother and sister had emerged into the great world of water and sky. Tripping on a twig halfway down the bridge, the third cygnet rolled and tumbled into the water and landed right side up beside her father.

The Old Cob collected the tenderest of pondweed and water beetles to offer to the first cygnet. The pond was shallow and swampy where the Cob and the cygnets were feeding. The Old Cob gathered food under the water for the three cygnets with quick jabs of his beak. He clawed with his big webbed feet to uproot plants and send them floating to the surface. His head turned frequently to survey the shore and pivoted to watch the sky. There were three infants to be guarded. The Old Cob could not leave his head under water long.

The Old Pen was trying to get the fourth cygnet out of the nest. This small, wobbly one nearly reached the crest three times, only to fall back again. At last the Old Pen pressed her beak against the nest and lifted him over the hump as if in an elevator. The surprised cygnet entered the water as the third one had, with a tumble and a splash and an outraged peep.

The Old Pen, trailing her wing, joined her family in the water. Swimming was easier than walking. On the water she folded against her side her wounded wing, caked with blood. Battered as that wing was, it did not look as if it would carry the Old Pen into the sky.

The first cygnet soon discovered that his beak was for eating, and that his father was stirring up the water so that insects, snails and bits of leaves and roots floated on the surface for him to grab. He gobbled these morsels. Soon his brother and sisters followed suit, often colliding with one another in a dive for a tempting bite.

When the Old Cob did not uproot the food fast enough for the first cygnet to get what he considered his fair share, he tried stirring up his own at the shallow edge. Thrusting his small pink bill down into the water and his fluffy tail up, he explored the mud until he came up with a delicious bulblet. Before long all the cygnets dipped and splashed among the sedge grasses, pulling up plants, bulbs and little shellfish.

When their appetites were satisfied the Old Pen would

lead them out for a swim. The cygnets followed her in single file, and the Old Cob brought up the rear.

One day, as the swans drifted about the pond feeding, the Old Cob and the Pen left the cygnets to paddle to deeper water beyond a screen of reeds. In the shallows the cygnets searched for worms. Suddenly from the air came a swishing sound as a shadow passed over them.

4: Airborne

FROM BEHIND THE SCREENING REEDS, THE OLD COB HEARD the swish. Instantly he acted, paddling back toward the cygnets. Pushing against the pond's surface with his feet, he spread his wings to their seven-foot limit, beating them as he tread the water. He hissed angrily.

He saw a flash of white on powerful, gull-like dark wings. Two long, forked tail feathers jutted out behind. Webbed and taloned feet stretched toward the cygnets. This was a jaegar, one of the fiercest birds of the northland.

The sudden appearance of the Old Cob confused the hook-nosed bird of prey. He veered off with a scream shrill as a cat's meow.

The Old Pen swam up beside her mate to watch over the frightened cygnets. The Old Cob settled on the water, still alert for another strike. The jaegar, however, did not return.

The jaegar's retreat was fortunate. If he had challenged again, the Old Cob would have had to take wing. It was his time of molting. Flight feathers in his wings already were beginning to fall out. A fast flight required all of his feathers in good condition.

He saw a group of swans flying over the channel to Richards Island. This was a colony of swans that were not raising families. There were juvenile swans, bachelors, old swans, swans who had lost their mates. Each molting season these swans flew to a remote, hidden place to spend their flightless days. They had formed this habit because their ancestors had been plagued by Eskimos chasing them in kayaks and on foot while they could not fly. The Eskimos liked their soft feather skins.

The Old Cob, with his cygnets and wounded mate, could not leave his pond. He must search out a hidden place within its shores.

By pulling up sedges and horsetails with their beaks and eating the tender parts, the swans cleared a concealed hide-away surrounded by vegetation. Their weeding even uncovered a large, domed muskrat house upon which they could loaf. The muskrat might have been a menace to the cygnets but for their watchful father. At first sight of the animal, the Old Cob chased him away with an angry hiss and a powerful peck of his beak. After that the muskrat kept his distance.

The Old Cob's wing feathers were among the first to be shed. Some of them he pulled out himself while preening. Within a few days all the big feathers of his wings were out. He took on a scraggly appearance. His tail feathers fell out and more and more feathers detached themselves from his body.

His body and wings were covered with about five thousand large, quill-like feathers. On his head and neck were about twenty thousand tiny downy feathers. The larger feathers were shed during this late summer molt; all through the year the smaller underfeathers were replaced.

The Pen, unlike the Cob, lost her power of flight during the nesting period. By the time the Cob became flightless, the Pen usually had her new feathers. If it had not been for her wounded wing, she would have been able to fly now and to defend the cygnets. However, her wing was stiff: she had not yet resumed flying.

The young swans, who had weighed only a little over six ounces when they were hatched, had increased their weight twelvefold within these few weeks. The perpetual daylight of the Arctic allowed them to eat twenty-four hours a day. At first the cygnets had preferred meat to plants, gobbling all the insects, worms and small shellfish they could find in their pond. Then as they grew bigger, they sought plants, submerging their lengthening necks to pull out roots and bulbs and tender leaves of water plants from the mud.

Feathers grew on the cygnets to replace their baby down. The feathers, except on their undersides, were not white, as they would be when full-grown, but had an ashy gray tinge. The cygnets would not become pure white like their parents until they were at least two years old. And as they grew, their beaks and feet got gradually darker, changing from the yellowish-flesh color to a purplish shade.

The Old Cob was starting to grow new flight feathers. They grew fast. The big wing feathers grew about an inch in every four days.

The whole swan family gathered strength daily, resting

and eating. Between meals the swans climbed upon the muskrat house. One of the parents stayed awake, while the other, crossing his long neck over his back, tucked his head under his wing to shut out the bright Arctic daylight. The cygnets did likewise, while the mate that stayed awake as sentry looked for movement over the blaze of color that at that season covered the tundra. Beyond the small fluffy white balls of cotton grass on the swampy muskeg shore stretched a riot of red rhododendrons and pink bog rosemary amid clumps of reindeer moss. Large piles of white clouds accented the bright blue of the sky. The fragrance of the flowers wafted over the swans on the muskrat house, and masses of birds flew overhead. This was a land created for birds. The songs of larks, screams of gulls, the weird cry of a loon and the melodies of hundreds of varieties of birds who nested here filled the air. Hidden among the plants were the nests, some still with eggs being hatched. The Arctic tern circled overhead.

The whistling swans, the largest of the waterfowl in the Arctic, were the first to arrive there and the last to leave, for their cygnets required a longer time to gain the strength and growth necessary for migration than did the young of the smaller birds.

The cygnets' wings were growing at a greater rate than the rest of their bodies. Sometimes the first cygnet and his brother and sisters felt they had too much wing. To them it seemed their wings were in the way. Wings were of no use in eating or swimming.

One day the Old Cob waddled off the muskrat house for

his daily bath. This was always an occasion for much family revelry. The Cob flapped his wings vigorously to douse himself with water. The Pen followed. Her wounded wing was still stiff. She had not tried flying with it. It did a good job of splashing, though.

The cygnets joined eagerly in the fun, wildly fanning their oversize, awkward wings.

The swans, once the great cascade of water produced by the propelling of their wings had thoroughly drenched them, dipped their heads and necks under the water, and then again began their wing-flapping. A dozen huge swan wings flashed up and down in a vast shower of crystal waterdrops. The Cob rolled over on his back in the water, still flapping his wings. This was a hard trick. The cygnets had some mishaps mastering this maneuver—wing collisions, bumped heads. The third cygnet rolled over on the fourth and gave him a ducking.

Soon all the cygnets were proficient at this part of the ritual of the bath. Often it exhilarated them so that they followed it up with a fast game of water tag. Wings outstretched, the Cob, pushing himself up on the huge black webs of his feet, ran across the water, while the Pen and cygnets took chase. To throw the pursuers into confusion, the Cob dove under the water and came up farther out in the pond. The five other swans bobbed under and up. Little circular eddies formed around them and merged together as they rose and fell like swans on a merry-go-round. At last the Old Cob came out of hiding and ran across the water again, his wings flapping, with all his family chasing behind. A shower of droplets trailed them as their beating wings picked up water from the surface of the pond.

It was on one of these merry chases that a surprising thing happened to the first cygnet. As he ran along beating his feet on the water, suddenly he felt himself lose contact with the surface of the pond. He was suspended above the water with nothing beneath him to hold him up! This gave him such a fright that he drew back his feet and fell into the water with a plop.

It was such a curious sensation that the cygnet tried it again, running at top speed, flapping his wings as before. Again he found himself hanging in mid-air over the pond. An awkward belly landing followed.

The Old Cob watched his son's first test-hops as he had watched those of many cygnets in years past. He preened his newly grown flight feathers, those delicate airfoils that were so sensitive to every trick of the wind—which showed him every force of the air—those vehicles which soon would carry him miles away to a place of plenty in winter.

The Old Cob, who had not flown for many weeks, made a take-off run and circled over the pond. Then he glided gracefully in, lowering his webbed feet to various angles to act as landing flaps that would settle him smoothly on the water.

It was the first time the cygnets had seen their father fly.

The Old Pen had not tried her wings either. She joined the Cob in a take-off. She rose cautiously from the surface of the pond. Although she could fly, her stiff wing was unpredictable in the turns and maneuvers. It tired easily.

Another member of the swan family had his difficulties when it came to flying. This was the fourth cygnet. Still smaller than the others, he had not yet acquired the combination of strength, speed, wingspan and confidence that it takes to get a swan into the air.

The cygnets were accustomed to playing follow the leader. Cygnets two and three soon took up the first one's game of soaring. The first cygnet often followed his father into the air, but he could not fly like his father.

The Old Cob glided smoothly from the air to the water while his cygnets came skidding in on their tails or landed on their beaks. How gracefully the Old Cob could execute circles in the air! What was his secret? When the first cygnet tried making beautiful arcs through the sky, his tail would not behave. It would tip, and when he tried to straighten it out, it would positively wobble. When his tail wobbled, his wings wobbled. The whole effect was not what he tried for. But he, with his sisters, followed unsteady courses through the air.

Practice would permit them to conquer the air. They would discover that the air is not flat, like the surface of a pond. They would find that it has invisible hills and valleys, streams, currents and eddies. They would find that the air has its forces, gentle and fierce, its winds, breezes and storms. They would learn to find the breezes, to live with the storms, to make the wind their friend. And they would learn to handle their own bodies, on which each feather has a function, as a student pilot learns to handle his airplane.

The fourth cygnet, however, could not even seem to get

into the air. When the other cygnets took off, he would splatter along with them, always bringing up the rear, and battling a choppy surface stirred up by the other swans' feet. With a great flapping and a rush of air full of drops from the top of the pond, they became airborne, leaving their bewildered brother in their slip stream, sinking back upon the water.

His wings had not grown large enough to support his body. He could not move them with just the right combination of power and coordination to get him into the air, and he couldn't get up enough speed on his take-off run.

He was not the only waterfowl in the Arctic to find himself in this predicament. In the long days of summer north of the fifty-fifth parallel, both animals and plants grow at a faster rate than they do in the temperate zones, where night comes to slow them down. It is no wonder that some of the birds do not measure up to this rate of growth. Each year there are some ducklings, goslings and cygnets who are not strong enough to fly by migration time. If the fourth cygnet did not fly soon, he would be among them.

Already many drakes were leaving the Arctic. The father ducks, unconcerned about their families' welfare, went off early to the south, leaving the hens to worry about the young. The hens would be along later with all the ducklings that could fly.

The fathers of the geese and swan families, however, stayed with them and guided them on the long journey to their winter homes.

Day by day, migrations of birds were leaving, first in

small flocks, then in larger ones. The songbirds were the first to go: their young had quickly attained the size needed to fly. Then the drakes, along with shore birds—the plovers and sandpipers. Finally even the hens and ducklings were leaving.

By now the sun swung lower for part of the day to be hidden behind the horizon, later to rise in a higher arc than it had done in midsummer. Frost penetrated the surface of the ground, killing the roots of some of the tundra plants, and the color faded from the landscape. The pond grew colder.

The fourth cygnet still could not fly. Meanwhile the other three cygnets were making great progress. They spent much of each day in the air and had developed speed, grace and skill in flying. They had learned to find the direction of the wind and to use it to help them gather speed as they flew. They had learned to go against the wind when they landed, and how to lower the webs of their feet at varying angles against the direction of the wind to make a smooth landing.

5: *The Slow One*

As the Old Cob and the fledgling cygnets soared over the channel, they saw the Eskimo camp beneath them. Arctic char fish were being netted and dried and stored away for dog food. Women were cutting up seals. The swans saw far below them two small figures making their way across the tundra toward their pond.

They were Quupak and Paasaak. In the weeks since Quupak and his friends had visited the swans' nest, the idea of taking a cygnet back to Inuvik to be a school pet had never left Quupak's mind. Now that he was about to leave the Arctic shore for the winter, he wanted the cygnet.

Quupak carried a cage with a frame of whale bones, and strips of hide woven in an openwork pattern around it.

The tundra was not so bright now. Patches of dried cotton grass emerged from the moss. The flowers were all dead. There were few calls and cries of birds. The ground was not so spongy beneath their feet, for the frost had come almost to the surface.

Quupak was good at finding directions. He had been trained by his father during their hunting and trapping days.

He put the cage on the ground as they neared the abandoned swan nest.

"They are gone," Paasaak said. They had seen swans in the air, but there was none on the pond.

"Maybe they are in the reeds," Quupak protested.

The Eskimo boys splashed about the shore. The fourth cygnet had seen them and was hiding now in the horsetails, his head down.

The two Eskimo boys moved stealthily through the sedge grass.

"No swans here," Paasaak said impatiently. "Let's go."

Quupak looked disappointed. As the boys walked around the edge of the pond north of the nest, Quupak saw a spot of grayish white through the tall reeds. He put his hand on Paasaak's shoulder. "Wait!" he whispered. "A swan, I think."

Quupak waded quietly into the water on one side of the clump of sedges in which the cygnet was hiding, Paasaak on the other. They moved forward.

Quupak peered through the tall grass. He spied the gray, downy swan.

The cygnet was in a tight growth of sedge. With an alarmed hiss, he tried to escape. His floundering only got him firmly entangled in the reeds.

The two boys grabbed the swan at the same time. In triumph they looked at each other. Between them they held his long neck and his wings close to his body while they carried him back to the cage and thrust him inside. The cygnet lay huddled with his neck limp. He tried to make

his abductors think he was dead so that they would dis-
card him. He bumped along uncomfortably in the cage,
which the boys held by straps between them, all the way
back to the Eskimo camp.

When the boys reached their camp, Quupak's father
looked surprised at the strange pet, and then he shook his
head. The camp was crowded already with all the meat
and fish and berries they had dried for winter. September
was here. Soon it would be time to go back to the settlement. A caged cygnet would only add to the confusion.

"You must kill him," Quupak's father ordered.

"But, Father, I want to take him to school. I got him for my teacher."

"He will die," the Eskimo father said. "You cannot feed a caged swan."

"I can feed him what he eats in the pond," Quupak answered.

The Eskimo father turned back to carving a little figure out of a piece of soft stone, his pastime while he waited for his nets in the channel to fill with char. He could sell the figures at a trading post.

"Do what you want," he said, whittling a corner off his block of stone. He wanted Quupak to learn by experience.

Quupak went into the tent. Across the back of it was the sleeping platform, covered with willow-twig mats over which reindeer skins were laid. All of the family, and sometimes visiting friends, slept together on this platform. In the center of the tent was a large oil drum used as a stove. Quupak could smell the fish drying on a rack over the stove. He took a bowl from the wooden box where his mother had neatly arranged their household utensils. As he went out of the tent, he saw that his mother had a big pile of moss drying for fuel inside the door. He stuffed his pockets with it. He planned to put it in the cage to make the swan more comfortable.

Quupak's mother was sitting outside the tent with a friend. They were chewing sealskins to make them soft. They would sew them into clothes. Quupak hurried past

her with only a grin and a grunt of greeting. He must feed
his new pet and make friends with it.

Down at the channel he waded among the mosses and
pulled up some water plants. Placing them in the bowl
with some water, he hurried back to the cage as fast as he
could without spilling the water. He hesitated to open the
the cage for fear his pet would escape. When the front of
the cage came off, the cygnet, however, did not try to get
out. He squeezed himself tighter against the back.

Quupak took the dried moss out of his pocket and spread
it over the bottom of the cage. He put the bowl of water
and plants near the front. Some children stopped a game of
kickball and came to see Quupak's new pet. The boy
watched a long time to see if the swan would eat his food,
but the swan would not. He stayed against the back of his
cage until Quupak and his friends became tired and went
away. After the Eskimos had gone, the cygnet came out
of his corner and gobbled the food. The smell of it had been
tempting him, but he could not move while the people
watched him.

"Hooray!" Quupak yelled when he saw the empty bowl
the next day. He ran to the shore to fill it up again. This
time the hungry cygnet was not so frightened. He ate
quickly with Quupak watching. Quupak filled the bowl
again and again. Soon the cygnet began to voice a hungry
croak when he saw Quupak coming. This gave Quupak
a warm, happy feeling. The swan was his friend.

When with a roaring and splashing an airplane on floats
landed in the channel to take the children of this Eskimo

camp to school for the winter, Quupak ran heavily to the plane, his canvas bag weighing down one arm and his swan cage the other. The cygnet bumped and tumbled about in his cage.

"What next!" the pilot exclaimed, staring at the swan. There was not much space for the children's luggage, much less this huge captive waterfowl.

"We'd better leave that here," he told Quupak. Quupak had grown to love the swan. He was determined to keep him.

"I am taking him to my teacher," he blurted.

The pilot gave way to the pleading of Quupak's eyes. "Okay, we'll try to find a place for it," he conceded.

So the cygnet's cage was wedged between two duffel bags on top of a pile of luggage in a flying school bus. The slow one, cygnet four, thus started flying south before the other swans—even before he could use his wings.

As the airplane roared through a few floating patches of cloud on its brief trip to Inuvik, the children in the airplane could not keep their eyes off the young swan.

The cygnet did not like this kind of flying. Once a bumpy stretch of air jostled his cage, knocking him against the side. He hissed and squawked. The children giggled.

Quupak, who was sitting near enough to the cygnet to touch his cage, comforted his pet.

"This trip will soon be over. You'll be all right then," he told the cygnet. "Everybody at school will help take care of you. We will get you food from the river or from our kitchen. Maybe we'll let you swim in the reservoir near the school. And next fall you'll be strong and grown up, and we will let you fly with the other swans to wherever they go in the winter."

The fourth cygnet inclined his neck toward his master and croaked approvingly.

6: Off to the South

High above the Old Cob's pond, a few flocks of geese flew in V-formation on their way south as the swan family came in and landed on the water. For the first time the fourth cygnet failed to swim out from the reeds to meet them.

As they swam about in their attempt to scratch up food from the now scanty supply on the pond bottom, still he did not appear. The Old Cob became restless. In the air he could hear the honking of migrating geese. He heard the soft, faraway musical barking by which he knew a flock of whistling swans was flying high overhead, coming from Richards Island.

The sky was a clear blue. The air had the fresh, zesty feeling that told the Cob it was high-pressure or anticyclone weather. A gentle breeze ruffled the sedges, pointing them southward.

As though following that direction, the Old Cob, who usually was silent upon the water, began to talk to his family in loud, strange notes. The Old Pen, who was preening her feathers with unusual care, answered in the same loud tone. The cygnets, excited by this new conversation, joined in with their high-pitched voices. They heard a swan call from a nearby pond, loud and strange. In a little while, from all about the tundra, the restless calls of whistling swans could be heard. The three cygnets quivered. With a wild scream and a loud wow-ou-ou, the Old Cob raced across the water and pitched himself into the sky, the Old Pen followed behind, and the three cygnets fell in line, answering him with their own shrill, piping screams. The swan family formed a ragged line, and some calling swans that also had just risen into the air joined onto the end of their line. Other swans increased the irregular row. When twenty swans had thus assembled themselves, like a white choir in the sky, the Old Cob, who was a little off center in the line of swans, rose sharply, seeming to pull the others along with him. He rose higher, higher, until the tundra's maze of ponds and channels and the polygon cracks that marked the crust of the western Arctic were like dots and hairlines beneath him.

When he found in the upper air a layer where the wind flowed a little faster to the southward, he leveled off. The air was cold. He tucked his black webbed feet up into his warm down and glided along on the stream of air, singing his soft, barking sound to the accompaniment of the other swans.

As the weird whistle of the migrating swans died away from the Arctic circle, the land which a few weeks ago had been gay and noisy with the calls and songs of hundreds of birds became silent. GFC

The snowy owl blinked and huddled into his white

feathers. A thick growth of soft down was forming around his legs and feet to protect him in the bitter winter, for he was one of three birds who would remain through the time of no sun. The ptarmigan was shedding his buff, russet and black summer attire for his thick winter coat of white. The rugged raven, however, would remain in the Arctic in his glistening black coat with his feet and legs naked as the ice advanced and the sun grew pale and the swans retreated on their long migratory flight south.

As the Old Cob rose to a thousand, two thousand, three thousand feet and higher with his family and the rest of the company of whistling swans, the horizons taken in by his wide-set eyes broadened. Before him he saw, on one side, the familiar banks of the wide Mackenzie River, dotted with hundreds of ponds, and the small, plain buildings of the settlement known as Reindeer Depot, with its backdrop of pines. The timberline began here. On the other side stretched the outlines of Eskimo Lakes, which separated Tuktoyatuk Peninsula from the mainland, and connected with Liverpool Bay. The great Mackenzie River would be his checkpoint through this long first leg of the flight.

He had first made this journey thirty years before as a cygnet. The outlines of this river and the lakes and ponds had stamped themselves on his memory. He had traversed this country on his way south so many times that the route unrolled before him like a familiar map.

From his point high in the sky over Reindeer Depot the Old Cob could see, from horizon to horizon, a distance of more than a hundred and thirty miles.

The Old Cob propelled himself through the sky with his

short wingbeats at fifty-five miles an hour. The wind moved at twenty miles an hour, which, added to the swan's speed, gave him a velocity of seventy-five miles an hour.

The cygnets trailed after their father. They had been flying for an hour. Their home pond had long ago receded from view when they passed over the town of Inuvik, with its neat, semicircular rows of white houses. They saw an airplane on floats landing on the Mackenzie River beside the town.

The Old Cob and the other whistling swans were not aware that the fourth cygnet was being unloaded from the airplane as they passed over it. The Old Pen was weary. She felt pain in her right wing. Unlike the cygnets, who expected that any time now their father would set his course downward, guiding them into a paradise of succulent water plants, she knew what lay ahead. Hours of flight without stopping until they reached a point five hundred miles south of their Arctic home.

Below her she saw scores of lakes, some glowing red with copper, some green with iron deposits. The broad, curving Mackenzie at Point Separation broke into a network of streams and marshy islands. This would be a good stopping place, but the rustling of wings and the call of the flying swans went on endlessly, and the delta with its many branches rolled itself imperceptibly over the horizon at the back of the migrating swans. Ahead, the curving river now was a single waterway.

As they passed the point where the Mackenzie fanned out into its web of streams and channels, they heard the melodious calling of another band of swans coming from the Yukon Territory to the northwest. The second flock fell in line behind the Old Cob and his companions, magnifying the sound of the wingbeat and the soft flight music.

As the Old Pen joined in the call of the flight, her voice at times had a mournful quality, and hearing this behind him, the Old Cob sensed the trip was hard for her. He could hear a little impatient complaining, too, in the shrill notes of the cygnets—but then cygnets always had that attitude at the beginning of their migration.

The Old Cob, who had been breaking the trail at the front of the flying wedge of swans now for more than two hours, fell back to let another cob take his place as leader.

Along the swan's route, a mixture of south wind with cold air moving down from the Pole formed a fog. At first the swans saw beneath them ragged patches of floating mist. Ahead they could see a fogbank stretching over the river and hiding the outlines of the landscape for miles inland.

Behind them the sun still glowed on the horizon. The swans proceeded toward the fogbank. But the fog grew higher as they flew. The sun grew pale with mist, then could not be seen at all.

The cygnets crowded closer to the Cob for fear he would be lost from view as were some of the swans ahead of them. The outlines of the river, swamps and ponds were gone. The weary Old Pen also crowded up toward her mate. Other swans in the flock were banding into little knots. The line formation became disorganized. The leader veered off in one direction, hoping to find a hole in the fog where something familiar might be visible. Other swans peeled off in another direction. They wheeled about in ragged circles, their calls now being more distressed than musical.

The cygnets saw two swans streak off from the noisily yelping circle and fade away into the fog. Where were they going? The milling circle became larger and every few times as it rotated, a number of swans would disappear into the mist.

At last the first cygnet, impatient with the aimless job of flying in circles and curious as to where the missing swans had gone, sailed off down through the dense cold wisps of gray fog. Down and down he went. He did not hear the cries of any of the swans. He was frightened and confused in a strange world with no ponds to see and a sky that was not like a sky. Where were the familiar voices of the Old Cob and the Old Pen?

The sharp eyes of the first cygnet seemed of no use to him. There was only this grayness before him.

Then he made out below some shapes close ahead—a group of silver circles that looked like water. The cygnet flew in eagerly to land on one of the puddles, setting his wings, adjusting his feet. With his landing came a shock. There was no pleasant splash of water, no refreshing cool-ness on his feet and underside. There was only a harsh, ringing thud, a bruising crash onto a hard, metallic surface.

The cygnet was dazed. His legs ached. He saw that he was perched some thirty feet above the ground on some-thing like a cylindrical cliff. There was no food, and he was alone.

He drew his battered feet up under his down and put his head under his wing to shut out the terrible, cold gray world.

7: Lost

Exhausted, the cygnet slept for nearly an hour on his odd landing field. What he had mistaken for a round pond was an oil storage tank that stood on the bank of the Mackenzie River at Norman Wells.

Presently he roused and stretched his neck up into the damp, gray air. For the first time in his life he was alone. He felt miserable and confused. Shakily he walked to the edge of the tank. Below, through wisps of fog, he could see a white thing on the ground. Spreading his wings, he soared down for a closer look. The thing was a dead swan that lay where it had fallen after striking a power line overhead. The cygnet poked at it with his beak. He drew back and turned quickly. Beating his wings, he flew on. His ears strained through the fog to catch some familiar sound.

A huge building loomed up in front of him. He veered off to the right, uttering a frightened cry. Flying on through the fog, he followed a course away from the building and the tanks. When they were well behind him he set his wings to descend, searching through the thick mist for the ground, alert for objects that might appear suddenly before him. As he made out the shape of a pond, he circled low above it before landing to make sure it was water.

The pond met his body with a welcoming splash. Swimming joyously around its irregular edges, he flapped his wings and doused himself with the cold water. He danced on top of the pond.

There were only a few scrubby, half-dead plants growing around the borders, and the plants were tough, unlike the food the cygnet had known on the Mackenzie delta. They could not nourish a famished, growing cygnet. The young swan, after his invigorating swim, took off to seek a better feeding place.

The fog clung fast over the river and its surrounding country. Peering through it, the cygnet vaguely saw another pond a few feet away. He pecked distastefully at the tough, dry vegetation around it, and soon left that pond, too, behind to set off on a journey of exploration, by foot and short flights through the relentless fog.

Now and then he saw tall objects leaning crazily above him. They were scraggly evergreens, whose roots, unable to penetrate the permafrost, grew horizontally so that the trunks made an angle with the ground. To the cygnet they seemed to be waiting in the fog for him to crash into them, or perhaps holding in their branches something that might leap at him as the jaegar had swooped on him long ago in his faraway home pond.

The cygnet moved in an easterly direction whenever he saw one of these tilted trees. He did not like high objects above him. Only when he could see in all directions around

him did he feel safe. He moved away from the riverbank.
The trees grew scarce and finally disappeared.

As he traveled, an eerie sound wafted through the fog,
seeming to follow him. It was far away. Was it the call of
a swan? It had the same high, yelping quality. Hope of
finding his family and companions leaped in the heart of
the cygnet.

He needed companions to help him find his way, to
search out food and safe places to swim. Turning back
toward the river, he was drawn toward the yelping song
that might be that of a swan. The muffled call of his own
kind was stronger than his fear of the obstacle course he
had just come through.

The sound disappeared, and then began again. Still flying
in cautious small flights, the cygnet continued his groping
forward. He saw fearsome objects again—a log cabin and
a tattered tent. Why would swans be here, in this maze
of dangers? Still the cygnet was lured on by the yelping.

The yelping became loud, and too close; it became deafen-
ing. All at once, the cygnet knew this was not the sound
of swans. As he landed on the ground after one of his brief
hops, he stared at advancing furry brown creatures with
yapping red mouths. They were pups from the husky-dog
pack which provided winter transportation to the Indian
family living in this log cabin.

Forgetting his caution, the cygnet made a hasty, helter-
skelter take-off run that took him straight toward the yelping pups. The little dog pack, amazed when the cygnet
spread his six-foot wings and advanced on them, thought

they were being attacked by this strange, hissing fowl. They scattered, protesting with shrill yi-yi-yis, as the cygnet, equally frightened, took off, grazing one terrorized pup with his big, black foot.

This topped the cygnet's day of fearsome adventures. He flapped to his full speed, climbing high into the fog. He forgot even the wires he had seen and the menacing trees. Though he could not see far ahead, he beat a path through the air that led over and between the hazards.

At last, with the town far behind him, the cygnet alighted on a secluded pond. Lonely and frightened, he floated, searching the icy shallows for food.

8: Up the Mackenzie

FOUR DAYS THE CYGNET STAYED ON THE LONESOME POND. HE
rested and ate, grew strong and forgot his troubles. At times
the fog seemed to grow lighter. Then it would "sock in"
again. The nights were long and cold.

One day a strong wind came from the north. The fog
blew by the cygnet, who had braced himself against the
wind on the edge of the shore. It stirred into shreds and
patches the thick gray fog blanket that covered the cygnet
and his world. At last the windswept wisps of fog sailed off
against a background of blue sky. The cygnet again could
see for a long distance about him. He soared up high to
survey the countryside.

Off in the distance, to the east, he saw the shoreline of a
seemingly endless blue-black body of water, the Great Bear
Lake, fourth largest body of water on the North American
continent. Already it was partially frozen: throughout the
year, the lake, gouged out by glacial action and filled by the
melting of receding glaciers thousands of years before, was
so cold that no fish could live in its depths. Only along its
shoreline could living things survive.

The cygnet was flying over a big, cigar-shaped lake whose ends pointed north and south. To the west he could see the oil tanks that had dealt him such a jolt. Beyond them and Norman Wells were the Mackenzie Mountains, with a foreground of dense evergreen forests.

A few geese were flying above the same finger lake the cygnet was exploring. Their noisy honking mingled with the sounds of waterfowl swimming below.

In the midst of the honking and quacking, the cygnet again thought he heard the musical tones of his own kind. He was flying low, and beneath him he heard a rustle of wings and the unmistakable whistling-swan call.

Three swans rose majestically into the air from a clearing behind the reeds. The cygnet followed them. Soon he had joined their group. It was a mother and father swan and their cygnet—not the Old Pen and the Old Cob, but the long-lost cygnet's loneliness was over. He had found the company of other swans again.

The swans' wings dipped and rose in the sunlight. The cygnet joined his calling to theirs. They sailed about a half mile up the shore to a small, reed-surrounded bay on which a few large white blobs floated. More swans! The cygnet's singing became louder and more joyous.

The four flying swans circled to face the wind, and came in for a landing, in precise formation. The first cygnet, although arriving in a place he had never seen, felt that he was home. Home, it seemed to him after his lonely adventure, was any place where he had the company of other whistling swans.

In his pleasure he rose up on his great webbed toes, spread

his wings and uttered some loud, happy notes which were strange to him. Other swans on the lake spread their wings and advanced toward the newcomers, also greeting them in a happy tone.

Among the fifteen or so swans in the bay, the cygnet saw the Old Pen and the Cob, with cygnets two and three following dutifully behind.

The Old Cob had been on this lake since the fog had closed in. He had been in fogs before, and had seen the pattern of the country so often in his migrations that he easily guided his family in to this lake. The Old Cob could tell while he was flying whether or not a lake was a good place to land. From the air he saw by its patterns of light and dark its shallows and depths. His practiced eye told him by the colors of green around the edges of a pond whether the plants there were good food for a swan.

Twice before he had landed in the area—once because fog had closed in, once because the upper air in which the swans had been migrating had been so cold and moist that ice had formed on the swans' wings. That had been a near disaster. Their wings had become so heavy they could not control them. The whole flock had crash-landed, many being dashed to death on the ground. Those who landed on the lake were saved. The survivors had continued their migration after their wings thawed.

That was a long time ago.

The Old Cob and the other old swans in the group had learned from their many years of flying the same route in the autumn that storms can come quickly and ice close in fast in the Arctic. When they saw the blue sky and felt the wind moving in the direction of their travel, they knew there was no time to lose. Their migration schedule already was several days late.

So the swans, after a noisy conference, again took off for a long flight up the Mackenzie River Valley. This flight, the Old Cob expected, would be easy. Since the first leg of their migration had been cut in half by the forced landing, this was really only half a journey; the next stopping place was on the western arm of the Great Slave Lake, a body of water almost as large as the Great Bear Lake they were leaving behind.

As they left the tanks of the town of Norman Wells below in the distance, the Mackenzie River, with its flat, monotonous banks, twisted and turned beneath them. For many miles the swans could see the Great Bear Lake in the east. They crossed a river connecting this lake with the Mackenzie, and passed the village of Fort Norman, with its government buildings clustered along the river among the huts, tents and log cabins of the inhabitants.

As the swans bore southward, passing Fort Simpson, where the Mackenzie was a mile wide, they began to see snow-covered country to the east. And at his first glimpse of their destination, the Great Slave Lake, the Old Cob saw its outlines were ringed with white.

The weary, hungry swans reached the island in the west arm of that lake to find their usual stopping place icebound!

9: Storm

AS THE OLD COB CAME IN ON THE FROZEN LAKE, HE TESTED it with his outstretched feet. He felt the surface ice give way beneath his toes, and retracted his legs, gliding in smoothly.

The cygnets, seeing a solid surface beneath them, were braced to land accordingly. They toppled in like water skiers taking a spill. What was this? Water with a shell? The first cygnet, dripping and surprised, chipped with his beak at the ice around the hole he had broken in his landing. About twenty swans—all that were left of their company— swam around him, amid wafers of ice. Some swans had never rejoined the flock after the mix-up in the fog. One group had cut off to fly eastward as they reached Great Slave Lake. They were going to a wintering ground in the eastern United States, and were taking a different highway through the sky.

The swans gabbled among themselves and explored under the ice for food. The ice had hit this pond from both above and below: while the top of the pond froze, the frost had killed off the vegetation around the edges. The Old

Cob snapped up a few small fish he found. There was nothing else.

Some of the swans walked up on the snowy island and explored it with their beaks. They had often found grasses growing under the snow. But on this island the edible plants were all dead. There were sounds of discontent among the swans, who had flown so far and needed nourishment.

The cygnets, however, had forgotten food in their fascination with this new-found element, the ice. They swam about like three tops in their clearing, now and then flapping their wings with pleasure. They climbed upon the crust of the ice, marching along until it broke beneath them, and then swimming about in the hole they had made. It was an absorbing game.

But after the Old Cob had rested his wings a while, he interrupted the cygnets' play with a sharp call that told them he was taking off again. The cygnets croaked complainingly. By now they expected long, high flights. Hungry as they were, they were not ready to make one now.

Nevertheless, they followed the Old Cob into the air. He flew low on this flight. He seemed to be surveying the long arm of the lake, going southward around the bends and bays.

The tired, hungry cygnets yelped piteously as they flew. The Old Pen's wingbeats seemed slower than the others. Once she fell back behind the family and the Old Cob slacked his cruising speed.

The arm of the lake widened and then merged into the

main body of the lake, which stretched off to the horizon. The Old Cob descended again.

Every year he had stopped for about ten days at the Great Slave Lake, and between feeding and loafing times, he had done some exploring. He had seen this point, where the Hay River flowed out of the lake. He knew there would be open water here. This was one of the secrets he held in his memory.

The Old Cob, who did not like towns, made a wide circle as he passed over the settlement of Hay River, and proceeded down its winding course searching for food with his sharp eyes. At last he let down at a hairpin curve in the river where the snow lay only in a thin, lacelike pattern along the banks. At this section of the river, the current had drained the cold from the soil so that the permafrost did not form as it did in most parts of the North. There was food here in this bend of the river. The Old Cob saw the color of it from the air. He led his hungry flock in. The swans hit the water with grateful cries. Their heads bobbed quickly into the water to snatch the long-awaited meal.

The day had started out overcast. Now a breeze came up. It blew away the clouds. The sky was blue, the air cold. The swans rested on the shore, calling to one another. Now and then they all slipped back into the water for another meal. Some folded their heads back under their wings and napped while others floated watchfully behind them.

The next leg of the swans' journey was to be strenuous. It led all the way down the province of Alberta across the United States border into Montana's Flathead Lake region.

Their long rest in preparation for the journey proved too long. One day a stiff breeze ruffled the Old Cob's feathers as he rested on the snow. Clouds scudded rapidly across the sky, piling up until they hid the sun, turning from white to gray to gun metal. The little ripples on the river grew into tall, angry peaks.

The Old Cob moved up on the shore as the water sloshed out of the river to dash against him. He had to brace himself against the force of the air as he walked. The cygnets, who had been swimming at the edge of the turn in the river, were tossed and buffeted against each other on the choppy water. They waded ashore and huddled against their parents. Sleet drove horizontally against them. A few dead reeds at the river's edge bent over so far that they snapped off and flew through the air.

Because they liked country with wide visibility the swans had chosen a place to rest where there were few trees or windbreaks. There was nothing to screen them from the storm. The pitch of the storm's voice rose to a howl. It carried a load of snow and biting sleet that covered the ground and hid the reeds at the bend of the river. It settled about the swans like a blanket. They shook themselves now and then to flick the snow and ice off their backs and heads. The swans could stand the cold, but they could not walk or fly in the battering wind. Old Pen and Old Cob had been in the snow many times before, as they waited in the spring for pond ice to thaw.

The wind raged on through the second day, although snow and sleet ceased to pelt the swans. Great blasts of air scooped up snow that had already fallen and sent it whirling again through the air.

When the wind's fury lessened, the swans walked through the snowdrift hills and valleys the wind had left. Their webbed feet were like snowshoes that kept them from sinking into the snow as they walked. They leaned with all their strength to keep from being flattened to earth by the wind. They went to the river to search for food, finding only water so wild that it drove them back into the shelter of a drift.

When at last the river calmed, the swans snatched a hasty meal of battered, half-frozen pondweed. Then, making up for lost time, they flapped on to the south—over the border into the province of Alberta.

10: Missing

THE PILOT OF A CANADIAN AIRLINER GLANCED OUT THE COCKPIT window. Between two layers of clouds he saw that he had company. Going in the opposite direction were more than a hundred and fifty whistling swans. He had never seen these large waterfowl before. It was a sight he would not forget. But, beautiful as the swans were, the pilot knew that high-flying birds have caused accidents by colliding with aircraft. He radioed the tower at Edmonton to report whistling swans at eight thousand feet.

The flock of swans, ten V-formations of fifteen swans each, also saw the big airliner. Their formations wavered in the sky.

The Old Cob, the Pen and their cygnets were again with a large flight of swans. Their little band had been increased by several groups that had flown in from Queen Maud Gulf to the northeast. Farther down, a few flocks coming from Lake Athabasca and down the Peace River joined them.

The Rocky Mountains loomed up to the west as the swans

passed over the fertile Peace River farmlands. Breaks in clouds showed them a country more populous than that which they had left behind.

The Old Cob and his family had come about three hundred miles on their journey from Hay River, but many of the swans with the group had flown even a longer distance before joining them. Some of these swans, as they approached the Lesser Slave Lake in central Alberta, began a letdown and all the swans followed along behind them.

Over the lake the flock milled and wheeled. Their hunger told them to stop and feed here for a while. Their tradition of flight to Montana beckoned them back into the sky. At last a group of some twenty swans that always stopped at this lake landed, while the others circled and called in uncertain, discontented notes. Then the positive, musical flight notes of the old, experienced birds sounded. The big flock soared back up into the higher altitudes to go on the more than four hundred miles that remained of their journey.

As they ascended, three irregular lines of swans that had rested long enough on this lake saw that these travelers were going in the direction of their own migration, and increased the Old Cob's group, joining their triple-noted call to the voices of the hundreds of snowy migrants.

To the east, the swans could see in the distance the buildings of Edmonton, the capital of Alberta, shining in the late afternoon sun. To the west were still the snow-capped Rocky Mountains which separated the province Alberta from British Columbia.

They had reached the south end of the province of Alberta

and were flying toward the mountains when the Old Cob suddenly felt something was wrong. For the last couple of hundred miles, he had been impelled along by the inertia of his own wingbeats. He had literally been resting in the air in the rush of wind stirred up by hundreds of wings of whistling swans. And now, with a sudden flash of awareness, he realized that a familiar voice was not sounding in the symphony.

He could not turn his head back to look, for in the force of air through which the swans were flying, they must keep their long necks straight ahead. His wide-set eyes saw behind him only a blur of scores of swans that filled the sky with their moving wings, and the Old Pen was not among them. When had she disappeared?

The Old Cob, though surrounded by hundreds of swans and followed by the cygnets he could hear yelping hungrily behind him, felt alone.

Night had fallen. The swans had seen the huge, orange moon of late October hover above the eastern horizon and rise to change into a cold silver disk that lighted the stream-laced country beneath them. The swans had crossed the Canadian-American border into the state of Montana. They sought the pass through the ten-thousand-foot Mission Mountain Range of the Rockies through which they always traveled. The icy peaks of the Missions stood out sharply in the moonlight. As the swans passed beyond them, they saw gleaming coldly to the west the familiar outlines of Flathead Lake, nestled in a valley ringed with towering, snow-crowned mountains.

The swans winged in on the valley and wheeled over the lakes and marshes to get their bearings. The various groups and families of swans began to disperse noisily, each to his favorite pothole, edge of the lake, or section of the marsh.

The Old Cob took his brood into a reedy pond near the big Ninepipe reservoir. Although it was night, the cygnets began eating the minute they slapped into the water, for this had been their longest journey. They had flown some seven hundred miles since the morning.

The Old Cob ate, too, but without the enthusiasm of the cygnets. He was restless. Flights of birds kept coming into the lake through the night, and with each new arrival, the Old Cob would scan the sky, expecting to see among the shapes, ghostly in the moonlight, the great white bird who had been at his side all these years.

At last he dozed on the lake, his head under his wing. Still, each time he heard the splash on the lake of a bird landing, he would start up, his neck erect.

The next morning the Old Cob with his cygnets flew over the familiar borders of the lakes on the Ninepipe and Pablo game refuges. They visited swans in many parts of the forty-five-acre preserve. Each time the Old Cob saw a group of the large, white snowballs in the landscape, he investigated anxiously. The swans would rise to welcome him and his cygnets as they landed, according to the ceremonies of whistling swandom. But the hoped-for familiar Old Pen was never among them.

11: The Trumpeters

WHEN THE SWANS HAD PAUSED AND HOVERED OVER THE LESSER Slave Lake in Alberta, the Old Pen had given in to weariness. As the big flock of swans, including the Old Cob and her cygnets, had soared up to altitude, she had struggled uselessly to stay with the Cob. She could not muster the extra strength it took to keep up with them. She cried out in vain to the Old Cob. The voices of swans flying away were so loud that her call was drowned out. Below her on the lake there was an even greater noise of swans landing. Exhausted, she circled down with the landing swans.

The Old Pen rested a day on the Lesser Slave Lake. It was an anxious rest, though. It was not right to be there. Swimming and feeding with these few strange swans, she was uneasy. It was not a place she had ever stopped with the Old Cob.

When a few days had passed, a strange family of swans rose from the pond. The Old Pen went with them. The family was late in its migration schedule. Two cygnets were late fliers, and the family had had to stop at every puddle in Canada to let the slowpoke cygnets rest and eat. The Old Pen, at least, had chosen company for her flight which was suited to her speed.

However, in attempting to catch up with their lagging schedule, these swans had chosen a day when the wind was not at its best. The little party flew against the wind. They flew low. The wind in the upper altitudes was too strong. Down below, friction of the earth slowed the wind so they would make more headway.

Still, the effort needed to fly was greater down here, with the air currents against them.

An unfamiliar scene flowed beneath the Old Pen as she traveled. Lakes, rivers and settlements that she never had seen passed below her. The swans were on a course farther east in the province of Alberta than the Old Pen was used to taking. She could see the town of Edmonton for part of the way. She was not far off course.

The swans, in this unfavorable wind, traveled only about forty miles an hour. In five hours, the shrill complaining and the weak wingbeats of the cygnets forced the party of swans down onto another strange lake.

After a few days of resting and feeding, the swans, with the Old Pen, took off once more. Again they went only a short distance, stopping at a lake in southeastern Alberta, just above the Montana border.

When the strange swans left this lake, they set a course due east. The Old Pen no longer could travel with them. They were going away from the mountains she must cross.

There were no other swans on this little lake, so she

must travel alone over the mountains and the vast stretches of land that lay on the route to California. As the swan family flew off toward the flat country to the east, the Old Pen instinctively turned westward, toward the mountains.

She searched for the familiar shape of the peaks she had always crossed to get to Ninepipe.

Following the strange swan family over their unfamiliar route, she had not begun her lookout soon enough. She had passed those peaks half an hour before, and was proceeding down beside the mountain range far to the south.

She was off course. She passed down a wide river that flowed by the city of Helena, Montana. Down one of its tributaries she flew. She could see awesome, snow-covered mountains both to the east and to the west. It was country she had never seen. She was not only alone, but hopelessly lost, with no landmark to guide her.

Weary, the Old Pen emerged from the mountains to find stretched below her a broad, snow-covered meadow, edged in the distance by forests of evergreen. Through the meadow a stream meandered, spilling out into shallow ponds at its sharp bends and curves. As she nosed down to lower altitude, she saw the white shapes of giant swans at one of the stream's overflowing elbows, and heard faint, eerie music like a distant band of French horns tuning up.

Eagerly she banked over the stretch of water, but circled in confusion as the trumpeting grew in pitch until it became a raucous din.

She saw pondweed in the water, and swooping close to the stream, caught the scent of it.

When her hunger overcame her fright at the noisy bugling, she lowered her feet to land, choosing a spot on the stream where none of the big swans was swimming.

As the Old Pen frantically dipped pondweed a gentle warmth in the water soothed her legs and body, cold from the icy upper altitudes. The warm springs of the Yellowstone area kept the stream pleasant, allowing food to grow all winter.

Evening was falling over the country. The big swans up the stream trumpeted without ceasing.

Although she thought herself isolated from the trumpeters, the Old Pen, as she pecked out pondweed, was the object of a fascinated gaze. A huge gray cygnet, making a trail of webbed tracks through the snow on the riverbank, had spied the dainty newcomer, and took to the water to give her a proper welcome. He flapped his wings, gave a high-pitched, off-key trumpet blast, and nodded his fuzzy brown head, which stood several inches above hers.

The Old Pen kept silent. This amazing cygnet was not of her species; she could not answer him.

The friendly cygnet pushed in closer to the Old Pen and continued to honk at her.

Other swans strolling on the snowy bank waded into the stream and circled with vague curiosity around the Old Pen and her friend, the trumpeter cygnet.

The Old Pen saw that the noisy swans were about a fourth again as large as her kind. Their faces were not like whistlers, for they had no yellow spots on their beaks near their eyes.

The big swans looked at their small cousin and floated off down the river.

The giant cygnet, however, stayed near her. Wherever she turned on the shallow stream, the cygnet followed. When night fell and at last the racket of the trumpeter swans was still, the Old Pen felt the cygnet close beside her.

In the morning, awakened by trumpet blasts which seemed louder than those of the night before, the Old Pen looked again into the admiring eyes of the big cygnet who had appointed himself her escort.

All morning he followed her, approving each morsel of pondweed or stalk of mare's-tail she consumed. When, in the early afternoon, the Old Pen felt the urge to push on from the pleasant resort of the trumpeters to find the winter home of her own species, the cygnet also pushed on, following her into the sky. It was only his own weight that separated him from the fascinating whistling swan; the cygnet's wings would not take his heavy body up over the fleecy cloud puffs where the Old Pen was flying. As she winged westward, her young companion turned back toward the home of the trumpeters.

12: Yellow Feathers

Meanwhile, at Ninepipe, trailed by his cygnets, the Old Cob continued his search for the Old Pen. At a small pond near the northwest corner of the reservoir, a myriad of ducks filled the air with their quacking. The cygnets had learned that wherever this many ducks congregated, the meals were good.

But when the Old Cob saw four scary monsters at the edge of the pond near the gabbling ducks, he set sail with his brood toward the far side of the pond, where he and his family watched the intruders with suspicion. The Old Cob had seen their kind before. They were his ancient enemy, like the ones that had come poking into his nest in the Arctic. Oddly, the ducks did not swim away from these men. In fact, they were flocking eagerly about them. The Old Cob saw the creatures shower some white food onto the surface of the pond. The ducks competed with one another to gobble the food. The cygnets looked on hungrily, but the Old Cob's manner told them to keep their distance.

The intruders were four Flathead Indian boys who were

eating their lunch at the refuge's picnic grounds. Their fathers helped to run the refuge.

The swans sensed, because of the actions of the ducks, that these Indian boys would not hurt them. Yet the Old Cob had learned to fear men. He soon took flight and returned with his cygnets to the marsh where they had first landed.

The days at Ninepipe were clear and calm. The mountains reflected in the lakes and ponds as in a mirror. The cygnets, after their recent struggles with the elements, grew fat. They could hear the chirping, quacking, honking and calling of a variety of ducks, geese and other birds. There were hundreds of thousands of birds here. It was like the Arctic at nesting time.

But the swans must push on. These waters soon would be frozen. One clear morning in the early part of November, the noisy voices of swans were heard on lake and pond and marsh. The preflight calls echoed and re-echoed against the mountains. A flock took off with a splash of water and a rustle of wings, and close behind them another flock fell into formation. Wavy lines of swans hovered above the ponds calling, singing, circling about; and flock after flock, they followed after those in the sky. The first group of swans had soared up high over the Bitterroot Mountain Range, and was lost from view when the Old Cob and his cygnets joined the line. The Old Cob felt strange and lonely to be starting off without the Old Pen. But the cygnets were eager to fly.

The great aerial procession flew high in the cold upper air above the clouds of winter all day, scarcely glimpsing the ground until they landed at the Malheur Lake region in southeastern Oregon.

When the Old Cob's family arrived, many swans already had landed on the island-studded lake. They greeted each swan as he glided onto the water with raised and partially outstretched wings and the whistling swan's welcoming notes. The lake rang with the noise of their happiness at seeing one another.

The Old Cob, who still watched the sky and searched the reeds anxiously for the Old Pen, flew about showing the cygnets this fine refuge, one of the largest in the United States, and hosting, at this season of the year, the greatest concentrations of birds to be found on the continent. Tall, snow-capped mountains rose to the east. Southward, the Donner und Blitzen River ran through a fertile valley. The cygnets also saw east of the lake old volcanic craters and fantastic columns and twisted sculptures of lava standing on the plains. Now and then, as the swan family flew over the sagebrush flats, they saw stately mule deer and white-tailed antelope grazing.

Distracted by his search, the Old Cob did not watch closely over his cygnets. They were nearly as big as he, and all of them, particularly the first cygnet, had become bold and adventuresome.

In their travels down the continent, they had found new delicacies in the ponds and streams of the various latitudes. The first cygnet had observed that a large group of ducks and geese at the water's edge usually meant that some tasty morsel was to be found there. One day the first cygnet followed a long parade of ducks and snow geese as they streamed into a narrow channel.

The cygnet explored the shallow bottom of the waterway. He had been used to eating leaves and roots, but here was something new. It was grain. The heads of the ducks and geese, with the cygnet's among them, rose and fell to gobble the amazing quantity of food they found here.

All at once an explosion sounded. The cygnet saw something like a cloud fly overhead. He must escape. He tried to raise his wings to find an open place to run across the water, but ducks and geese were crowded all about him. His wings would not go up. Something was holding them down. His head was stopped from going all the way up, too. All about him, ducks and geese flapped wildly but uselessly. No birds could fly. They were caught in a trap!

The waterfowl had forgotten about the delicious food. No one was eating. All were crowded together, colliding with one another, looking for an open place on the water where they could swim away and escape.

The cygnet, the largest of the birds in the trap, felt the most confined. It was he, with his long neck, who first saw the men approaching. Instinctively he tried to flap his wings and to get his feet above water. All the other birds tried to flap their wings, too. There was a din of honking and quacking. The cygnet hissed at a goose that brushed his face with her struggling wings.

The panic among the waterfowl increased as the men came near. They were carrying big wire boxes and wore wading boots up to their waists. They waded into the channel at one end of the net.

"A good catch," one of the men remarked to the other.

"There are a lot of snow geese here," the other man added. "And look, there's a whistling swan! We can turn these white birds over to the color-marking project."

The man reached carefully for the big, frightened swan. His experienced hands soon had pinioned down the powerful wings. The cygnet found himself occupying a wire cage with a pressing, squawking lot of snow geese. He felt a bump as the captor set the cage down on a truck bed, and a terrifying roar as the motor started. The cygnet shrank, paralyzed with dread, into a soft, seemingly lifeless mass of geese which quivered, swayed and jolted with the truck over the uneven back roads of the refuge.

A jerk ended the truck ride, the cage swayed up and out with its inert occupants. The cygnet felt the biting cold change to an unnatural warmth as the cage again was set down. He heard the snap of a latch and saw a goose flap wildly out the cage door, only to be caught again and held by a man. The cygnet and the rest of the geese cowered in the cage, but one by one, the man pulled them out. The cygnet put his head under his wing as his turn approached. The man reached in with both hands and held him so firmly that the cygnet could find no way to resist. As the one man gripped him tight, the other prepared to do something to the cygnet. The surprised swan took his head from under his wing and watched the man thrust a yellow brush toward him and with it softly stroke the feathers of his breast, and then stroke the yellow brush lightly on his wings. A peculiar aroma pervaded the air.

Held captive, and still being brushed, the cygnet looked up. The sky was gone. A roof had shut it out. The ponds and marshes were not to be seen. Walls hid them. The geese that had been his companions in the small cage now walked cautiously about. But they were not the same as they had been. They were colored pink and green.

At last the men released the cygnet and he was free to roam in this larger cage. He felt a chill. It was not the refreshing cold of icy ponds or fresh-melting snow, but a cold which came from the acrid wetness of his feathers. The cygnet turned his long neck to preen the moisture away. His feathers had been painted bright yellow.

And now that the men had colored all the geese and the swan, they opened a door and went out, closing it behind them.

The waterfowl walked about the room, pecking at the wall, or at chinks of light at the door, looking for a place of escape. The chill of his skin and feathers left the cygnet as he began to dry. Slowly the light left the waterfowls' prison, and the cygnet saw many geese huddling together, drowsy in the pleasant warmth. Again the cygnet put his head under his wing. Sleep soon blotted out his fear and confusion.

When he awoke, bright-hued geese were milling about pecking at grain which had been left on the floor. Presently the men returned. But they did nothing to the geese or the swan. They simply opened the door, and at the sight of the sky, the birds rushed pell-mell, squeezing all together into the outdoors, where they ran and waddled and flapped eagerly into the sky with glad cries. The cygnet soared high above the others.

"The yellow will be easy for us to spot from airplanes," one of the men remarked, watching the swan's graceful flight. "The pink looks pretty good, too. We ought to be able to track their migration route for sure this season."

The cygnet, ignorant of the fact that his yellow coat was for the good of science, alighted at a lonely pond. He dipped his neck in as far as it would go. He rolled over. He splashed and doused himself thoroughly. His yellow coat stayed yellow. Wading ashore, he preened himself, and still remained yellow.

He flew up again, seeking to join his family, and yet reluctant to join them. He was different from the others now. Circling warily over the pond, he saw the Old Cob and his sisters and groups of other swans on the water. At last, risking the reception of an unwanted intruder, he landed with his flock.

The Old Cob stared at his cygnet. His sisters raised their wings and, with other swans, circled about him filling the air with musical cries. His new yellow coat made him the most interesting bird on the lake.

He spread his huge golden wings and uttered a joyous song to his friends.

13: Rescued

By now the Old Pen had left the home of the trumpeters. With her weakened wing, knowing that she might be forced down by fatigue, she was eager to keep her eye on a handy landing place. She followed the Snake River.

Although there were no familiar scenes on the ground in Idaho, the Old Pen was determined to find her way to the Old Cob and her traditional wintering grounds. Since the land failed to yield a clue to her whereabouts, she looked to the sky. She had learned the angle the sun made at her winter home at various times of day. That knowledge led her westward, around the many curves that gave the Snake River its name.

Now and then she encountered a scattering of wild ducks. A few snow geese, also, had alighted along this river. And once, as some ducks and geese rose from the water, she heard the shattering sound of hunters' guns. There was danger and fear in the Old Pen's journey. She stopped often, but not long, to rest.

Once when the Old Pen's wing had begun to fail her, she came down upon the river and tucked her head under her wing to rest. The current carried her slowly closer and closer to shore, following its course among water-polished stones, now and then bringing her near a clump of sagebrush on the desolate shore. The shadows from the afternoon sun were just beginning to lengthen. A shaggy-coated coyote, his face resting on his paws, patiently watched the hole of a ground squirrel. He had not been able to find a meal on this barren prairie throughout the whole day.

He turned his head as a flash of white came into the corner of his eye, and saw the white swan asleep on the river. He saw how the eddies in the river carried the big fowl close to shore. The ground-squirrel hole forgotten, he stole silently toward the bank of the river. He crept closer around the clump of sagebrush, where he waited, eyes agleam, for his dinner to travel over to him.

All was silent as the swan drifted near. There was only the gurgle of water moving over the river stones. The coyote tensed for the spring, his eyes sharp and greedy. His teeth were bared. Only a few feet more.

At that moment from the sky a hum like a giant bumblebee broke the stillness. The coyote, when his wait had almost ended in success, felt a rush of panic at the noise. He lunged toward the Old Pen. His foot slipped, and a stone noisily splashed into the river.

Snatched from sleep, the Old Pen jerked her head up. Her great wings spread. The murderous jaws of the coyote snapped at her while the air thundered with a crackling roar. The hum the coyote heard had become a shattering, ear-splitting racket. A great shadow, a fantastic rattling whir descended on the coyote and the swan. An incredible bird swooped down out of the sky.

In panic, the coyote scrambled for cover. The startled Old Pen, now fully awake, pushed wildly against the river's surface and flapped along until she was on the wing. She had soon left the dreadful scene far behind her.

The great bird that had parted the predator and his prey was a light airplane. It had been cruising about this country at low altitude, piloted by a biologist who was taking a wild-life census. His eyes were practiced at distinguishing the shapes of animals and waterfowl on the ground and water. He had quickly sized up the situation of the coyote and the swan, then had kicked the rudder and pushed down the stick to buzz the coyote.

The pilot smiled as the coyote scampered off across the brush. He turned to watch the graceful white swan sail on in her course up the Snake River.

The Old Pen knew from the position of the sun in the sky that she was winging north in her trail up the Snake. But still she felt safe only if she kept the waterway in view for an emergency landing. She crossed the state of Idaho and arrived at the Oregon border, where the country began to awaken secret chords in her memory. She had come to a scene that she knew. She was back on her migration route.

She left the Snake River, and within a few miles, she saw two shapes: the rounded Harney Lake to the west; nearer, the irregular outlines of Malheur. She was no longer lost.

She came in upon the section of Malheur where she and the Cob had landed each migration. Weary as she was, she did not stop to rest or eat. She swam among the reeds searching, searching. Where was the Old Cob? She hunted restlessly for a long time, then stopped to eat.

14: Freeloaders

THE OLD COB AND THE CYGNETS HAD LEFT MALHEUR SEVERAL days before. As they flew that November afternoon out of the big refuge and over the plain of dead volcanoes toward California, their number had increased to hundreds of swans. Their multiple voices produced a continuous soft whistling, and the slow downbeat and quick upbeat of their wings made a mighty rustle. The yellow cygnet was a strange splash of color in the procession of gray and white that moved swiftly over the sky.

They crossed miles of the Great Sandy Desert of Oregon and rose over the Cascade Mountains. They passed over Crater Lake in Oregon and over still more dead volcanoes as they crossed the California border. Down the valley which had the Sierra Nevada Mountains to the east and the Coast Range to the west they streamed. The inhabitants of towns beneath them could not see the swans because an autumn haze hid the birds from view. They heard the high-pitched drone of the soft voices, which, traveling in the wing-fanned wind, sounded like a long-drawn-out whistle from the ground. Lewis and Clark, the explorers, had heard this whistle on the Columbia River in Washington, and had given the whistlers their name.

In the town of Willows, California, the people had gone to bed about an hour earlier. A tremendous racket awakened them. More than a thousand swans were descending over their town to land at the ponds and marshes of the Sacramento National Wildlife Refuge. The celebration as swans who had reached the water greeted landing swans was wild and raucous. Swans danced on the water with big quivering white wings partly extended into gull-like V's. Their long necks were erect, stretched to their fullest height, as they voiced the whistling swan's greeting call. They had reached their journey's end. They were thousands of miles from their summer home in the Arctic. In the temperate climate of California they would spend the winter.

The Old Cob led his cygnets to a marsh edged by a jungle of cattails. After the cygnets had rested and had a breakfast of tule roots, they explored the islands, ponds and channels which were to be their winter home for as long as they lived. They shared the marsh with dozens of mallards, pintails and widgeon ducks. As the sun rose they heard a rustling in the cattails. Hundreds upon hundreds of red-winged blackbirds emerged, peppering the sky with their swift-moving shapes. Gorgeous rainbow-colored ring-necked pheasants scuttled out of the bulrushes near them and ran along the dikes banking in the marshes. Now and then they whirred into the air for a low flight.

The November sky was gray the first morning. Only a few leafless willows and cottonwood trees rose from the flat land on which the refuge was located. The cygnets liked their new home. The Old Cob, however, found it lonely to be in these familiar surroundings without the Old Pen.

Long ago, the huge Sacramento River Valley had been dotted with wilderness marshes, the home of waterfowl. Gradually the marshes had been drained and the rich river-bottom land used for agriculture. At some seasons of the year more than two million birds were squeezed into ten thousand acres that had been set aside as a refuge. There was, therefore, a great scramble for food on some of the ponds. The refuge managers planted fields of grain near the ponds and marshes to provide enough food for the waterfowl.

Once the first cygnet scratched out a tender root with the claws of his strong, webbed foot. As he waited hungrily for it to float to the surface, an alert diving duck gobbled it from under his beak. The cygnet gave the duck an angry peck and the duck paddled away with a bit of the delicious root still trailing from his beak.

The cygnet tried again. Head down in the water, he pecked up a clump of green stems and surfaced to enjoy them. His head no sooner hit the air above the pond than a circle of ducks, squawking competitively, pulled the stem strand away from him. He watched in annoyance as two ducks played tug-of-war with one of his reed stems.

He turned his back on the thieving ducks, angrily twitched the tip of his tail, and moved away. The ducks followed him. Sometimes the cygnet, struggling to loosen a tenacious root from the mud at the pond bottom, found the ducks had dived down to grab a share even before he had got it up to the surface. It was maddening to work so hard without a swallow of food.

The cygnet turned on the ducks and attacked them with

his wings. He tweaked a feather from the tail of one. They retreated, but experience had shown him it was not for long. They would return.

The cygnet waddled disgustedly out of the pond and across a sandbar to another section of the marsh. As he swam through the water in a maze of cattails, he heard the quacking of many more ducks, and saw a dome of wire above the water. Inside, ducks were feeding eagerly.

A gleam came into the cygnet's eye as he remembered the taste of the grain in the trap at Malheur. He swam along the edge of the wire. When he came to an opening, he paddled in and soon was sharing the ducks' grain.

A truck pulled up on the dike above the wire dome. Two men got out, with a boy who always came with them on Saturday when there was no school. As he jumped out of the truck, his galoshes oozed into the soft marsh, but a mat of fallen and broken tule reeds kept him from sinking in farther. A narrow path had been chopped through the cattails and a wide board laid down for a bridge. The boy hurried down the bridge, between cattails high over his head.

At the end of the board he reached the domed feeding trap.

"It's full, Father!" the boy shouted.

At the boy's approach, the air was filled with quacking.

"Father, here's a strange one," the boy called, spotting the yellow swan.

The boy's father was coming down the plank through the cattails with his wire crates to get birds for banding.

He laughed when he saw the big yellow cygnet.

"Hey, look who got caught in our trap," he called to his companion. "One of those yellow swans from Malheur."

"How do you know he's from Malheur?" the boy asked.

"He's yellow. Malheur is the only place around here dipping them yellow."

"Why did they dip him?"

"To find out where he goes. The men counting waterfowl all over the United States and Canada can easily pick him out from the air. They'll tell us whenever they see him in his travels. They can find out where he spends the summer. One time I heard of some buffalo being painted yellow so that pilots could find out where they went, too."

"Yellow buffalo?" The boy grinned. "How could anyone dip a buffalo?"

"They couldn't," his father answered. "Someone flew over a buffalo herd in a helicopter and sprayed their backs with yellow paint."

The boy threw back his head and laughed.

"You stay there on dry land," the father continued to his son, as he waded into the water. When he reached the far end of the wire dome he opened the gate. As before, the waterfowl were quacking, honking, hissing and throwing themselves into a pile-up at the opposite end of the trap. The refuge man filled one cage with mallard drakes and another with mallard hens. By separating them he could easily keep records of the types of ducks he would band.

"Get outa here, you!" he said to the cygnet. The big,

awkward fowl, flapping his huge wings, clambered to the top of the pile of ducks.

The bird bander deposited his crates on the board walk and shooed the cygnet out the door and into the air.

When the banders returned that evening on another round of their traps, there in the center of the captive water-fowl once more was the bright-yellow cygnet!

Again the bird banders threw him out, and again he waited behind the cattails watching their truck disappear, so he could sail back into the dome of delicacies. The greedy ducks, flapping and shoving, spoiled his pleasure. So he developed a trick, as he went through the hinged door to the trap, of feeding close by the door and blocking it with his huge body.

Dozens of pintails and mallards honked and quacked in discontent outside the trap. At last the cygnet ate his fill without interference.

When the banders returned, no birds except the unwel-come yellow cygnet awaited them. One man muttered un-happy words under his breath, and then chuckled in spite of himself. The other went half grumbling and half laugh-ing back to headquarters to get supplies for making the door smaller. When the men had remodeled the trap, its en-trance was just large enough for a duck or goose. The swan could not squeeze his huge body in.

As the cygnet, deprived of the easy life he had found, rounded the tules into his own little clearing, he saw, floating close together, the Old Cob and his mate.

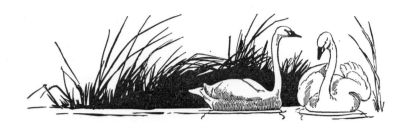

15: Together

FROM MALHEUR, THE OLD PEN KNEW HER WAY TO THE SACRA-
mento refuge, but could not make the trip in one flight as
the Old Cob and the cygnets had. Her stiffened wing forced
her down three times. When at last she soared over the
cattails into her home of thirty winters, her eyes sought out
the companion she had been searching for these hundreds
of miles.

There in the familiar clearing she saw him. Her wings
trembled with joy as she landed in the water and glided up
beside him. They floated side by side around the marsh
where they had spent so many days, and were unaware of
the noisy cygnets clamoring around them.

The cygnets flapped their wings and pranced on the water.
The yellow cygnet showed off his golden plumage.

Back together again, the swans spent the days of winter
happily and lazily. For long periods they preened themselves and loafed on the shore. Then they ate, tearing out
the big cattails with their strong legs and feet.

If it had not been for the swans tearing out and eating so

many cattails, these plants would have taken over the swamps, filling the clearings until the water disappeared. Even so, crews of men often came out onto the marshes when the cattails got too thick and removed some of them to keep the marshes from disappearing. They were glad when the swans did this job for them. The muskrats helped some, too, by gnawing away the plants.

The big swans with their long necks and strong feet could get food when the ducks and geese could not reach it. They usually found enough food in the water. The ducks went into the fields beyond the marshes to hunt for the grains of rice in the stubble that had been left after the harvest. The refuge men had planted these fields so that the ducks and geese would not trespass on the lands of the nearby farmers.

Early in the autumn, when the first ducks came down from the north and the grain was still ripening on the stalks on neighboring farms, the farmers had a hard time keeping the ducks out of their fields. When too many ducks dropped in for dinner, the farmers hired airplanes to scare them away and herd the birds back to the refuge. The pilots dropped exploding firecrackers from the airplane to scare them more.

The swans liked to feed in the water and seldom went upon land to find their food. Once they followed the ducks and geese out of the refuge on their feeding flights around the Sacramento Valley. In leaving the refuge, they encountered danger. They flew into a volley of gunfire.

The Old Cob felt a searing pain in his right wing but he flew on desperately. One of the swans was struck fatally. As the swan plummeted down, down, out of formation, the flight call that it had been singing in chorus with its companions changed. Notes the swan had never voiced before poured from its throat, forming a song of weird, unearthly beauty. The swan's last, lovely song echoed off the water below. The music seemed to expand to fill the air, to entwine itself about the cattails and to still the sounds and calls of other birds on the marsh.

The hunter hiding in the tules listened awe-struck as the song swelled about him. He had heard the expression "swan song" used to describe someone's last great effort in life. Now he actually heard the fabled song of a dying swan. It was as if the swan had distilled all of its wild, soaring existence into its music.

When the swan splashed lifeless onto the water, the music remained, in all its perfection, in the mind of the hunter. He stopped his hunting and regretfully picked up his supplies and trudged away. In all his life, he never forgot the last song of the swan.

High overhead other swans increased their wingbeats to flee from the hated sound of gunfire. They were cut off from their ponds and marshes. The men, with their deadly instruments, were between them and the refuge.

The Old Cob saw a section of marsh out in the distance. He set his wings to land with the other swans following him. The marshy pond which the swans approached was ringed with hunters, guns poised, hidden in the reeds. A few artificial ducks were on the water so that it looked like a safe pond for waterfowl.

This time the swans came in with not a shot being fired. They had been recognized as swans.

The Old Cob and the Pen and their family and companions floated upon a pond which belonged to a hunting club near the town of Willows. The hunters were allowed to shoot certain numbers of ducks and geese each year so that the waterfowl population would not grow too great for the amount of food available to them on the refuges.

The day was gray, and a little fog lay on the surface of the water. Mixed with the brackish scent of water plants, the swans could smell the acrid odor of gunpowder and smoke. They felt afraid on this pond.

The Old Cob signaled to his companions to lie low. They were not to fly again until nightfall. Meanwhile, the swans swam warily around the lake, always close to a reed bed so that they could not be seen. They did not eat for fear of rustling the cattails and advertising their presence to the hunters. At nightfall they rose and returned to their own safe clearing.

At last when January was half over, the hunting season in California ended and the sounds of guns were heard no more. Vast flocks of birds from the refuge took to the air to soar freely over the Sacramento Valley.

However, the Old Cob was not among them. The shot which had gone into his wing did not keep him from flying at first, but later it distorted his muscle. Try as he might, he could not get the wing to take him up off the water.

Heavy rains came. New puddles and marshes appeared on the refuge. The old ones grew into deeper lakes. New water plants appeared in them, to the delight of the swans. Polliwogs wiggled by, and a crop of tender young snails hatched. The leaf buds of the willows and cottonwoods were swelling.

The cygnets were as large as their parents. But they looked as if they had grown out of their clothes. They still had the feathers they had produced a year ago, but their bodies were much larger. As they grew, the white roots of their feathers were exposed. Some of their brownish-gray feather tips had faded in the sun and weather of the year past. The young swans had a mottled appearance. Even the yellow swan looked patchy, with white roots showing on some of his golden feathers.

The days began to lengthen. The frost that formed during the clear nights quickly melted away after the sun rose.

The cygnets now and then saw some swans on their pond behaving strangely. They heard a new tone in the voices of some—a loud cry which quivered across the water and then grew softer and died away. They saw young cobs prancing about on the shore with their wings spread and their necks arched, showing off before young pens. Sometimes the cygnets saw these cobs fighting. They saw one cob chase another, attacking him with wing and beak, trying to pull out his feathers.

The cygnets looked on curiously. They were too young for such activities. New courtship calls of other birds on the refuge sounded above the fields and marshes.

The cygnets heard the rattle of the herons' feathers as they skimmed low over the ponds. The pheasants bustled busily about the dikes.

As spring approached the birds on the refuge became more active, except for the Old Pen and Cob. Often when the flock from their pond took wing, one swan following the other into a quivering line in the sky, the old pair would remain paddling in the water or would wade up on shore, there to plume their feathers. But the cygnets felt the excitement of spring and followed the other waterfowl in their restless flights.

The swans were more impatient than the other birds to be first to arrive at their faraway nesting sites. The northward migration would not be a relaxed, sociable flight, as the southward one had been. Parent swans would peck and quarrel with their old cygnets, trying to get rid of them to be free for the new clutch of cygnets.

Toward the end of February, a few pairs of swans sent their flight calls ringing over the marshes and winged like jets, their cries whistling behind them, into a cloudless blue sky to the north. Their departure sent a wave like panic through those that remained. A great hubbub began among the swans. Flock after flock splashed and flapped over the water's surface and lifted themselves into the air.

The high music of hundreds of swans sounded all day, becoming soft and far away as swans disappeared beyond the horizon, and mingling with the louder music of others just leaving the water.

The cygnets circled about restlessly on the marsh, flexing

their wings with annoyance at being left behind. The Old Pen and Cob floated over to the shore and waded onto land. They plucked at their feathers. Out of habit the cygnets came ashore and clustered about their parents, waiting for them to lead them into the sky.

The Old Cob could no longer fly, and the Old Pen's flight powers were limited. It was time for the cygnets to migrate north with the other swans.

The Old Pen pecked angrily at the yellow cygnet, raised herself, flapped her wings and hissed at the other two cygnets. The Old Cob strode on the shore. Still the cygnets hesitated.

The Old Cob advanced on one of the cygnets and gave him a sharp jab with his beak. He attacked the others in the same way. The Old Cob's purpose got across. The cygnets waded into the water and echoed the preflight call they had heard so often in days past. Their huge, mottled wings pumped noisily up and down on the water. Then, airborne, they sailed over the cottonwood tree that stood on the edge of their marsh. A flock of swans, their white wing-tips accented by gray shadows under them, moved off in the distance. The cygnets raced to catch up with them.

The Old Cob and the Old Pen floated near the shore with their necks stretched, their beaks up to watch the cygnets. Suddenly the urge to migrate which had sent him to the Arctic thirty times took possession of the Old Cob. Loudly he uttered the migration call of the whistling swan. He pushed against the water with his feet. He spread his wings and ran. Drops of water danced and played after him as his feet and wing-tips ruffled them from the top of the pond. He ran and he ran. He reached the edge of the marsh, then turned and furiously swam back to his starting place. He ran again, vainly working his wings against the unyielding air.

Migration fever also hit the Old Pen. She echoed the Old Cob's desperate flight calls and ran after him. Her wings bore her up and up through the layers of the air. She saw below her the pattern of dikes and ponds, marshes and meadows, and beyond, a broad valley to cross. But she heard from below her the beseeching flight call of the Old Cob.

The Old Pen banked for a turn. Gently she glided in and quietly landed beside the struggling, splashing Old Cob. As she came close to him, the Old Cob's wings stopped their flailing. The pair sailed serenely on the marsh together.